The Classical Piano Method
Duet Collection 2

Hans-Günter Heumann

ED 13486

www.schott-music.com

Mainz · London · Madrid · New York · Paris · Prague · Tokyo · Toronto
© 2012 SCHOTT MUSIC GmbH & Co. KG, Mainz · Printed in Germany

ED 13486
British Library Cataloguing-in-Publication-Data.
A catalogue record for this book is available from
the British Library.
ISMN M-2201-3349-7
ISBN 978-1-84761-278-6

Cover design by www.adamhaystudio.com
Cover photography: iStockphoto
Printed in Germany S&Co.8811

CONTENTS

1. The Musical Children's Friend

Op. 87, No. 35

Heinrich Wohlfahrt (1797-1883)

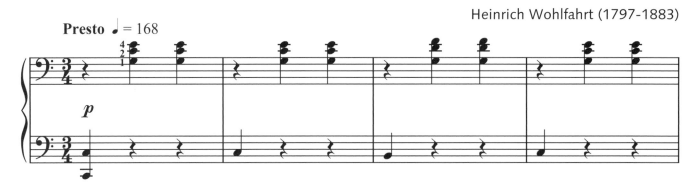

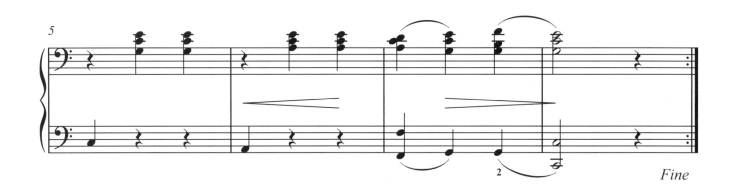

Fine

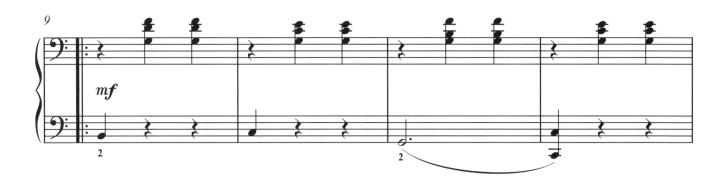

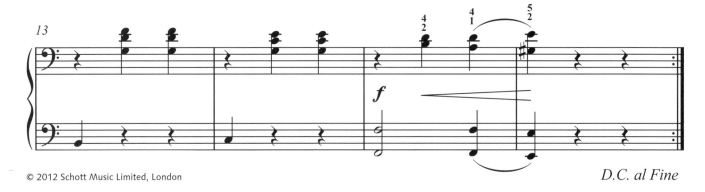

D.C. al Fine

Primo

1. The Musical Children's Friend

Op. 87, No. 35

Heinrich Wohlfahrt (1797-1883)

Presto ♩ = 168

Fine

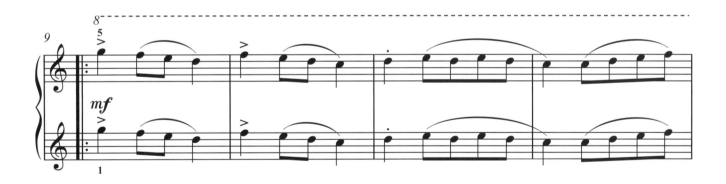

D.C. al Fine

2. Scherzo

from *Melodious Exercises* Op. 149, No. 6

Anton Diabelli (1781-1858)

2. Scherzo

from *Melodious Exercises* Op. 149, No. 6

Anton Diabelli (1781-1858)

Fine

from: A. Diabelli, Melodious Exercises op. 146, Schott ED 9009

Trio

Scherzo da capo al Fine

Trio

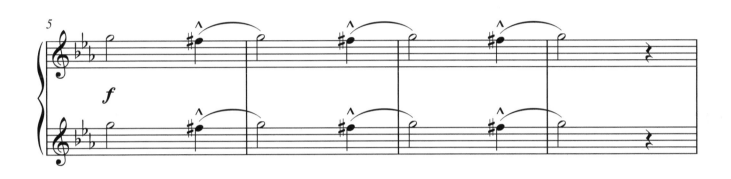

Scherzo da capo al Fine

3. Rock It

Hans-Günter Heumann

3. Rock It

Hans-Günter Heumann

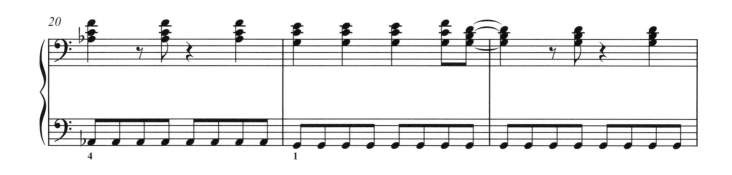

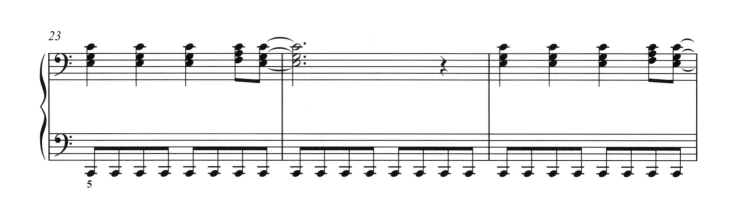

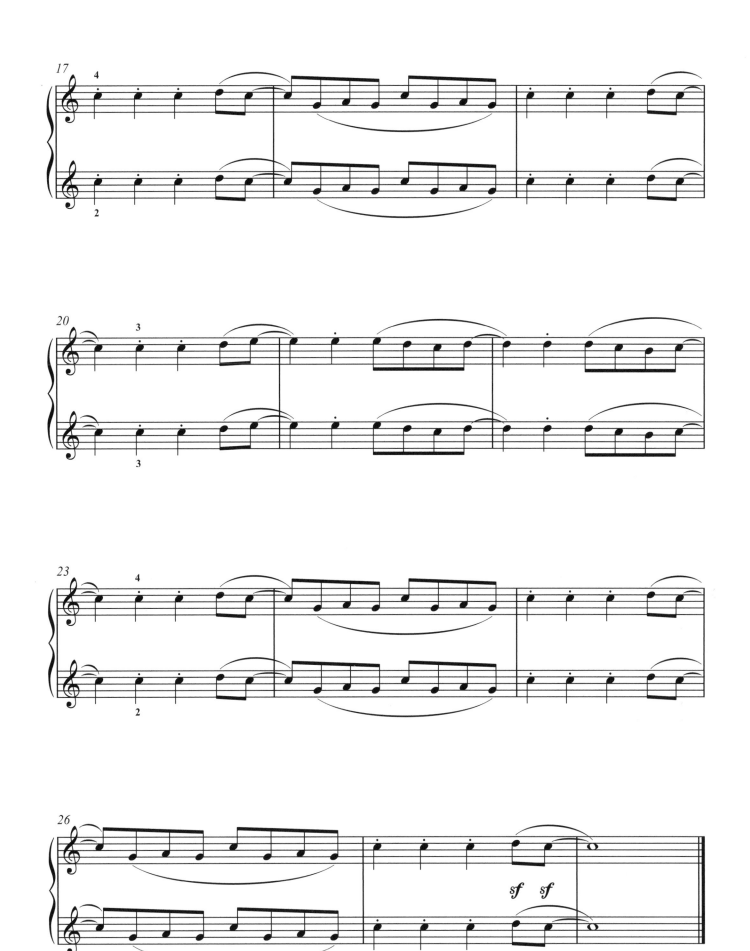

4. Melodious Exercise

Op. 149, No. 4

Anton Diabelli (1781-1858)

4. Melodious Exercise

Op. 149, No. 4

Anton Diabelli (1781-1858)

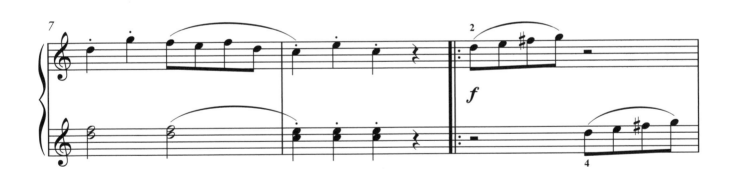

from: A. Diabelli, Melodious Exercises, Schott ED 9009

5. German Dance

Ludwig van Beethoven (1770-1827)

5. German Dance

Ludwig van Beethoven (1770-1827)

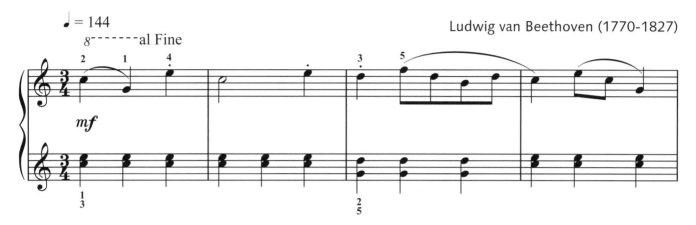

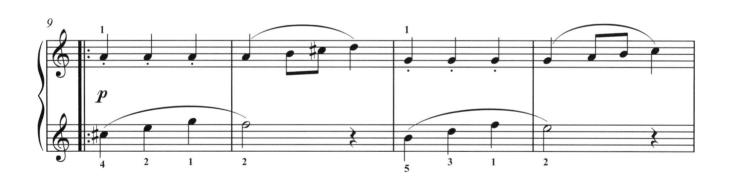

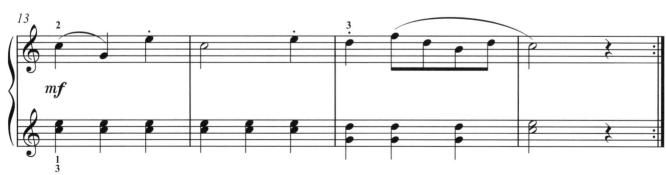

6. Ländler No. 3

K 606

Wolfgang Amadeus Mozart (1756-1791)

Arr.: Hans-Günter Heumann

6. Ländler No. 3

K 606

Wolfgang Amadeus Mozart (1756-1791)
Arr.: Hans-Günter Heumann

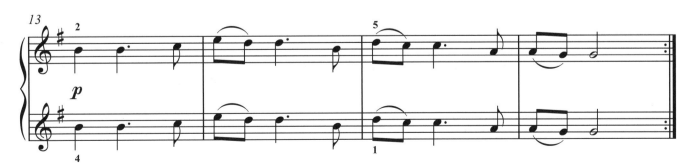

7. Little Piece No. 1

from *Three Little Pieces*

Anton Bruckner (1824-1896)

7. Little Piece No. 1

from *Three Little Pieces*

Anton Bruckner (1824-1896)

8. Go Down Moses

Traditional Spiritual from the USA
Arr.: Hans-Günter Heumann

8. Go Down Moses

Traditional Spiritual from the USA
Arr.: Hans-Günter Heumann

9. Fairy Tale

Op. 98, No. 1

Alexander Gretchaninov (1864-1956)

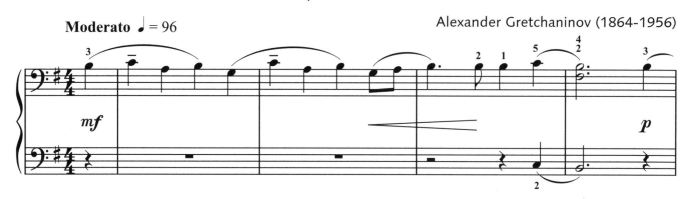

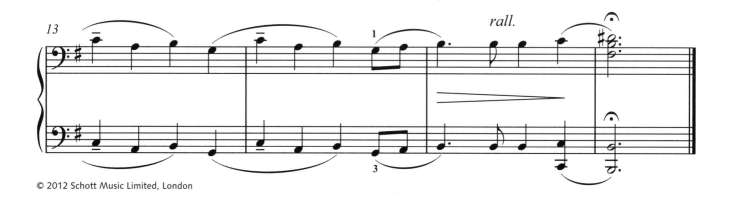

9. Fairy Tale

Op. 98, No. 1

Alexander Gretchaninov (1864-1956)

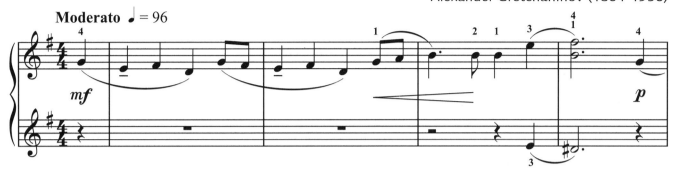

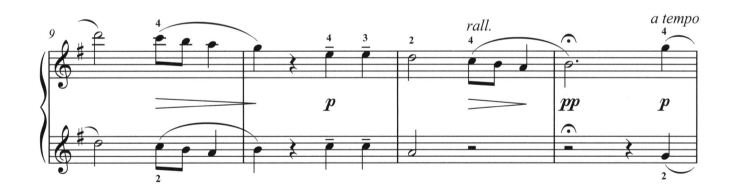

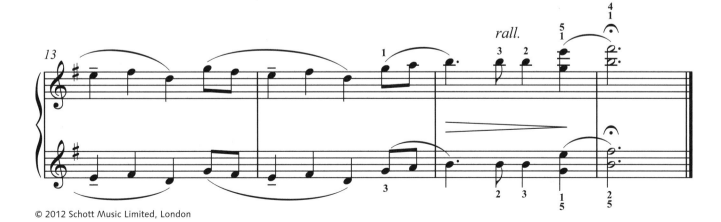

10. Lascia ch'io pianga
(Let Me Weep)

from the Opera *Rinaldo*

George Frideric Handel (1685-1759)
Arr.: Hans-Günter Heumann

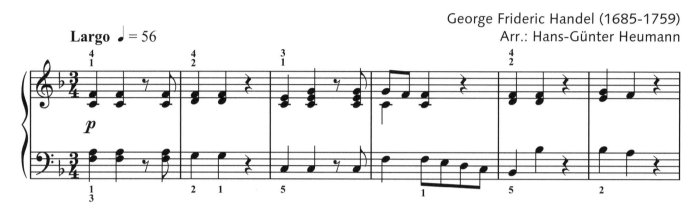

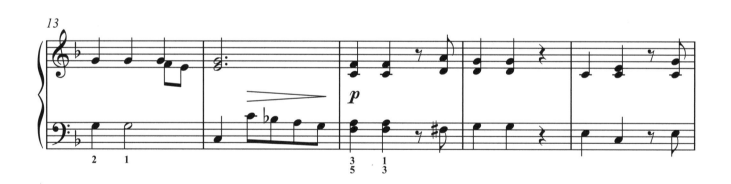

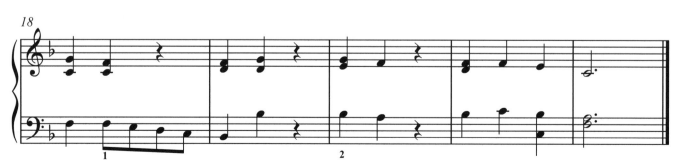

10. Lascia ch'io pianga (Let Me Weep)

from the Opera *Rinaldo*

George Frideric Handel (1685-1759)
Arr.: Hans-Günter Heumann

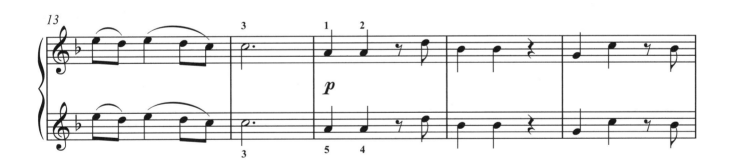

11. Wade in the Water

Traditional Spiritual from the USA
Arr.: Hans-Günter Heumann

11. Wade in the Water

Traditional Spiritual from the USA
Arr.: Hans-Günter Heumann

*) Students can also play a C natural if they prefer.

12. Ländler No. 1

Franz Schubert (1797-1828)
Arr.: Johannes Brahms (1833-1897)

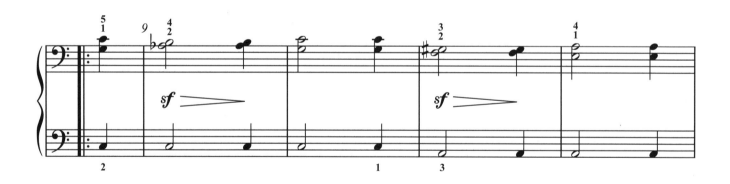

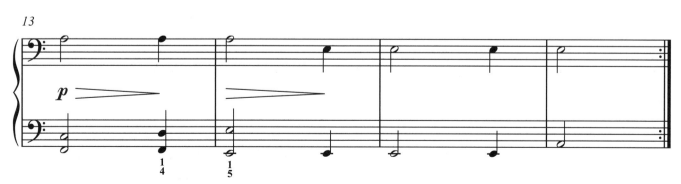

12. Ländler No. 1

Franz Schubert (1797-1828)
Arr.: Johannes Brahms (1833-1897)

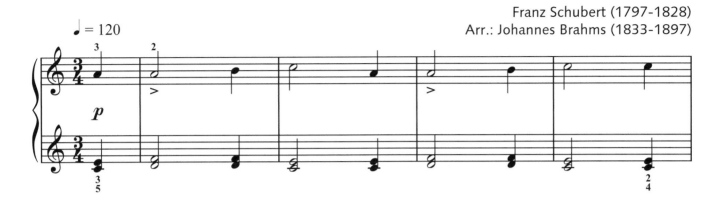

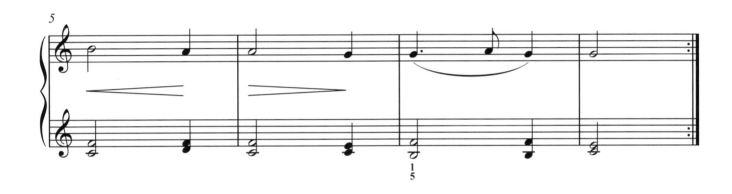

13. Mexican Hat Dance

Jarabe Topatio

Mexican Folk Song
Arr.: Hans-Günter Heumann

Fine

D.C. al Fine

13. Mexican Hat Dance

Jarabe Topatio

Mexican Folk Song
Arr.: Hans-Günter Heumann

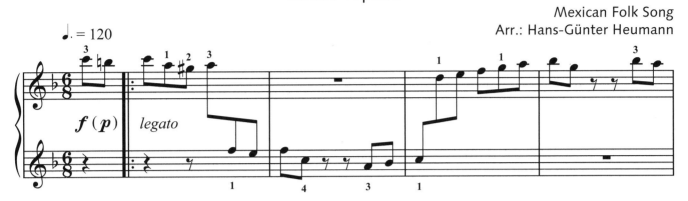

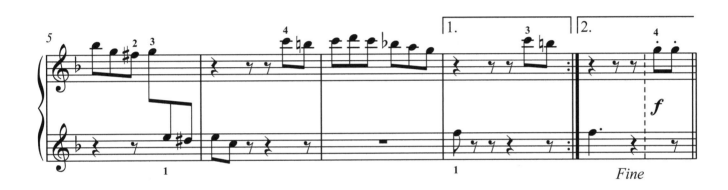

D.C. al Fine

14. Allegro

Johann Baptist Vanhal (1739-1813)

14. Allegro

Johann Baptist Vanhal (1739-1813)

15. House of the Rising Sun

Traditional from the USA
Arr.: Hans-Günter Heumann

15. House of the Rising Sun

Traditional from the USA
Arr.: Hans-Günter Heumann

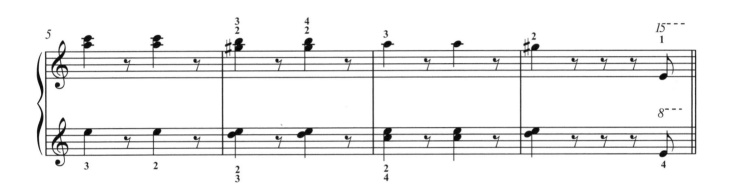

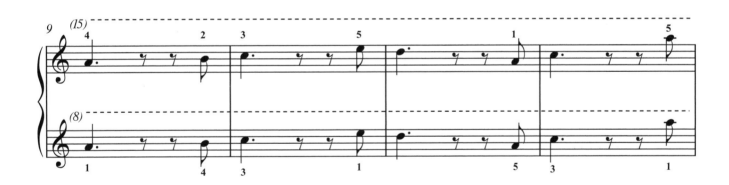

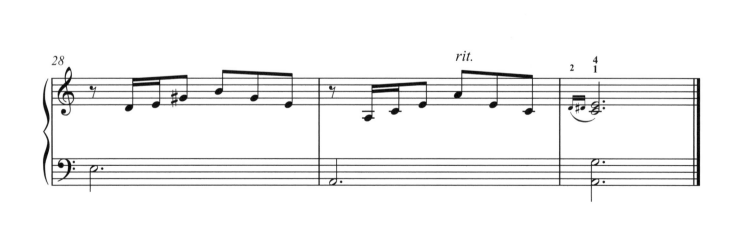

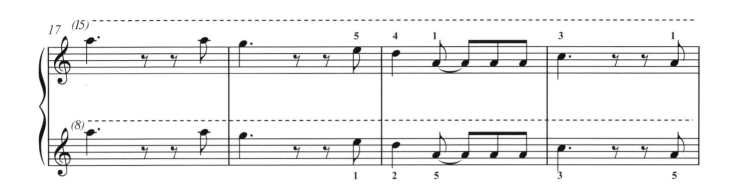

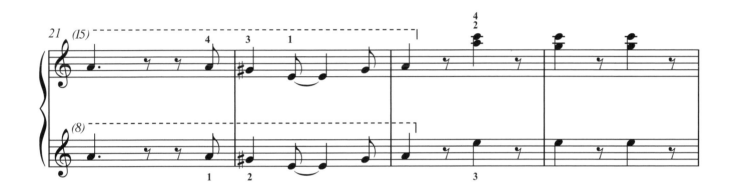

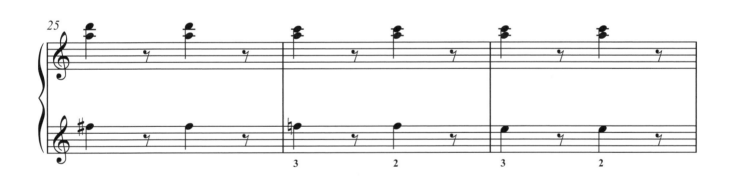

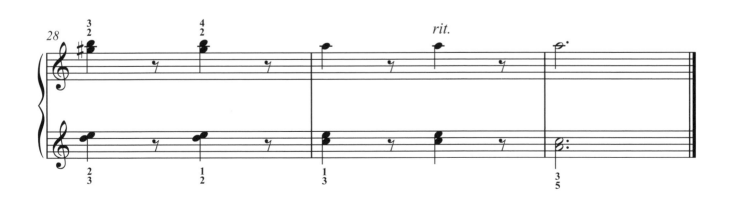

16. Alla turca

Op. 149, No. 26

Anton Diabelli (1781-1858)

16. Alla turca

Op. 149, No. 26

Anton Diabelli (1781-1858)

17. Peasant Dance

from *The Beginner* Op. 211, No. 17

Allegretto scherzando ♩ = 96

Cornelius Gurlitt (1820-1901)

Fine

17. Peasant Dance

from *The Beginner* Op. 211, No. 17

Cornelius Gurlitt (1820-1901)

Allegretto scherzando ♩ = 96

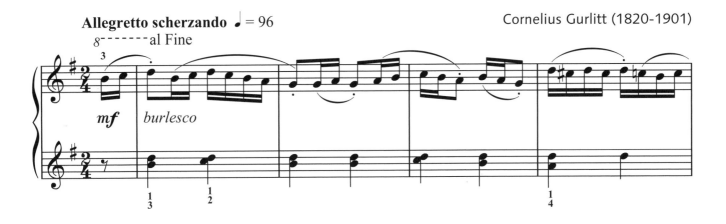

Fine

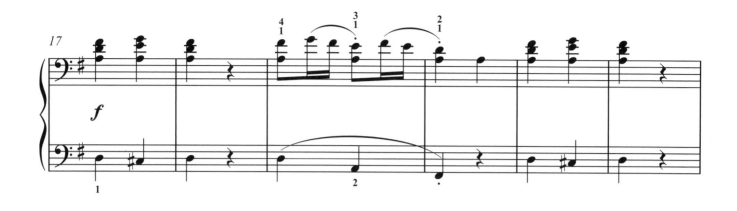

D.C. al Fine

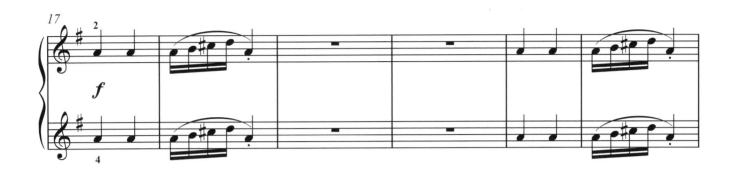

D.C. al Fine

18. Boogie Piano

Hans-Günter Heumann

18. Boogie Piano

Hans-Günter Heumann

19. Allegro

Op. 149, No. 28

Anton Diabelli (1781-1858)

19. Allegro

Op. 149, No. 28

Anton Diabelli (1781-1858)

20. Triumphal March

from the Opera *Aida*

Giuseppe Verdi (1813-1901)
Arr.: Hans-Günter Heumann

20. Triumphal March

from the Opera *Aida*

Giuseppe Verdi (1813-1901)
Arr.: Hans-Günter Heumann

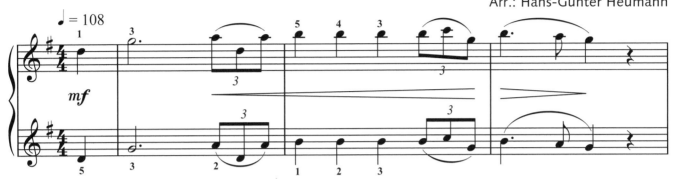

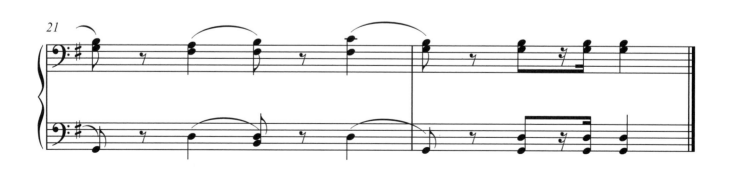

21. The Easy Winners

Ragtime

Scott Joplin (1868-1917)
Arr.: Hans-Günter Heumann

Fine

21. The Easy Winners

Ragtime

Scott Joplin (1868-1917)
Arr.: Hans-Günter Heumann

Fine

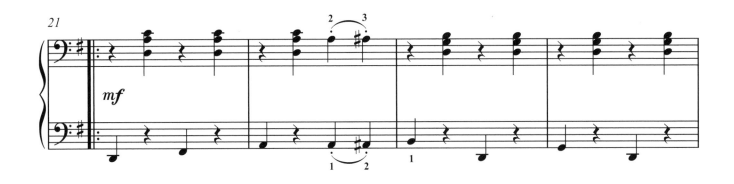

D.S. al Fine

D.S. al Fine

22. Clarinet Concerto

Theme from the 2nd Movement, K 622

Wolfgang Amadeus Mozart (1756-1791)
Arr.: Hans-Günter Heumann

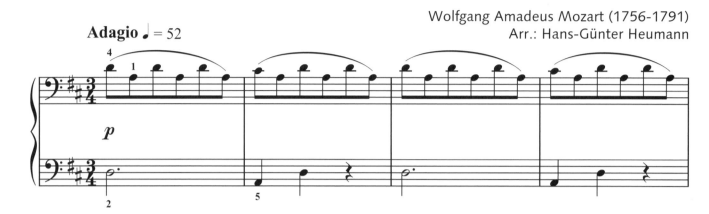

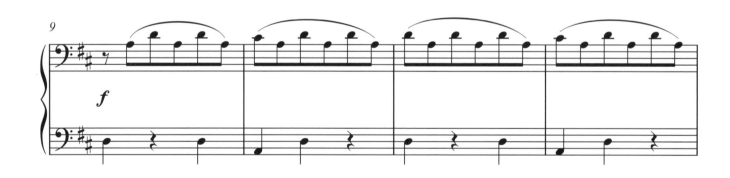

22. Clarinet Concerto

Theme from the 2nd Movement, K 622

Wolfgang Amadeus Mozart (1756-1791)
Arr.: Hans-Günter Heumann

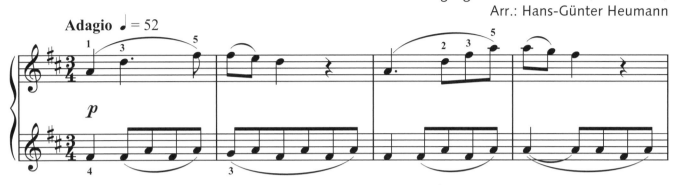

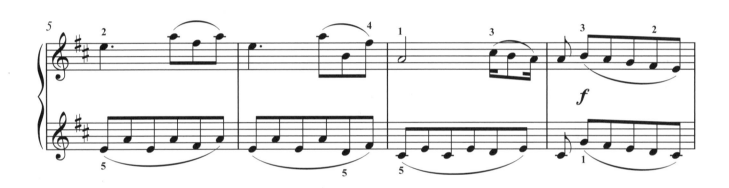

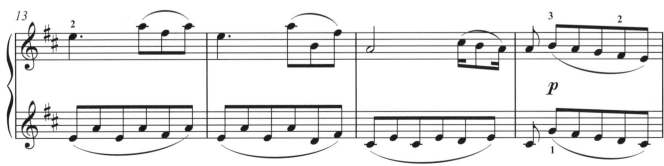

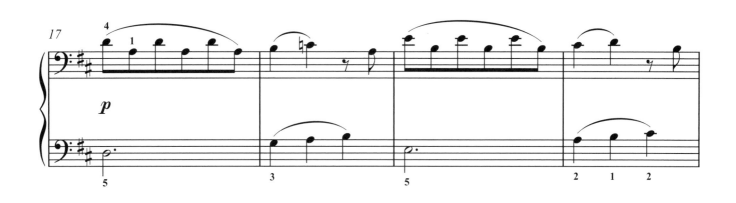

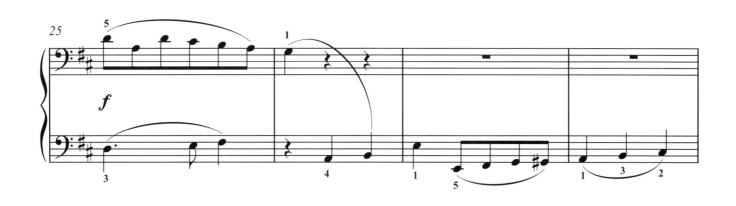

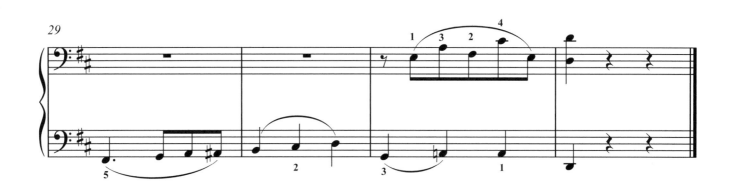

CD Track Listing

Recording Acknowledgments

Recorded October 2011
Piano - Samantha Ward, Maciej Raginia
Engineered and Mixed by Ken Blair, BMP recording
Produced by Ateş Orga